The Magical Forest of Aliveness

A Tale of Awakening

By Mary O'Malley

Awakening Publications
908 3rd Street
Kirkland, Washington 98033

ISBN 978-0-9720848-5-7

Editing, front cover design and layout by MarySue Brooks

Illustrations for 'The Clearing,' 'Opening the Heart,' and 'The Field'
were created by Kathleen Okamoto, a local artist in Kirkland, WA

Illustration for 'Return to the Village' is included courtesy of
Karen Brown's World of Travel (www.karenbrown.com)

This book is dedicated to every person who is consciously on, or ready to embark upon, the journey into the magical forest of their own aliveness.

Table of Contents

Once upon a time there was a little girl named Rose who was born in the Magical Forest of Aliveness. In the center of the forest was a village called Mind, where Rose lived with her parents in a sweet little cottage beside the wall surrounding the village. She was so curious! Everything was brand-new and full of wonder. Imagine what it was like for her—the mosaic of light as it shifted throughout the day, the music of voices, the smell of warm milk, the rush of sensations as she was touched.

Rose loved their magical little cottage. As she learned to crawl she explored every nook and cranny. She delighted in hiding under blankets and playing peek-a-boo with her mother, and oh, the fun of rubbing her food in her hair! She was also very happy pounding on things and putting them into her mouth. There was no past or future in her mind, so every moment was full and rich and fascinating.

Even though she loved living with her parents in their snug little cottage, as she grew older, Rose felt a longing for something more. She wasn't sure what it was, but she knew she would recognize it as soon as she saw it.

She started to explore her neighborhood, and one day she discovered the wall surrounding the village. Somehow she knew that what she longed for was on the other side of it. Following a faint path, she discovered a secret garden tucked in the shadow of the wall. As she entered this special place, she saw trees and flowers and grass and bugs and birds. She felt such joy, for none of these things existed in the village. She became enthralled with the wonder of it all—dewdrops clinging to spiderwebs, tiny flowers with iridescent petals, and soft green grass. She came back every day and spent hours lying on her tummy, watching ants going about their work, raindrops trickling down leaves, and flowers opening and closing.

Then the most amazing thing happened. Behind all the lush plants in this garden, she discovered a tiny hidden door in the wall, only big enough for a young child to pass through. The first time she stepped through the door, she knew that she had found what she was longing for. There before her was the Magical Forest of Aliveness. Very quickly she ran across the field and entered this unknown but somehow familiar world. She felt so at home in the forest that every day, as soon as she woke up, she went to the secret garden and through the hidden door, spending all her time becoming an intrepid explorer of the forest. There were paths to follow, fields of grass to lie down in, little streams to dip her hands and feet into, and trees to climb. Her body glowed with the joy of it all.

Because she was fully present for life, when she sat by a brook, she knew that it was singing to her. The birds flitting through the forest were her friends. Rather than just seeing trees, she was able to feel them, each one expressing a different essence. Everything was an important and necessary part of this Magical Forest of Aliveness, and she wanted to get to know it all. Rose felt completely at home here, for she knew that she was safe and that she was an important and necessary part of the forest too.

Every night she went back through the hidden

door, into the village of Mind. The longer she stayed in the village, the more her head filled with thoughts. At first they were as fascinating as the sound of the wind in the trees. They hadn't yet completely filled up the space within her, so she could still be fully awake to her life in the village. To put her head on her puppy's chest and to hear the rhythmic beating of his heart filled her with love. And to be cuddled in her father's arms when the evening darkness would begin to enfold them brought indescribable joy.

Of course she experienced anger, sadness, and fear, but she didn't hold onto these feelings or resist them, so they moved through her like the clouds in the sky, barely leaving a trace. No experience was rejected or held onto. It was just life flowing through her, and it was all good. Sometimes her mother would come to the secret garden, and Rose felt that in the garden her mother could see and feel the aliveness and the joy that Rose knew so well. But her mother never stayed very long, and she never even noticed the door in the wall that opened into the Magical Forest. Rose longed for more of this kind of connection with her mother, but it rarely happened. In time, she began to see that all the adults around her were too busy to really be with life, but this didn't make sense to her, because Rose could see that they were missing the joy and aliveness of life.

Late one night she heard her parents talking, and in curiosity she crawled out of bed and crept up to their door. She heard her mother saying, "I think Rose has found a way out of the village and is exploring the forest of Aliveness, for she is gone for long periods, and I can't find her anywhere in the village. We cannot let little Rose out of the confines of the village anymore. She doesn't understand that there are dangerous creatures like lions, tigers, and bears in the forest and that they can hurt her."

As her father agreed, Rose's chest began to constrict, and for the first time in her life fear got stuck inside her. As she crawled back into bed, rather than feeling safe and warm under its cozy covers, she felt afraid. She didn't quite understand why she should be afraid of the lions, tigers, and bears. Whenever she had come across them in the forest they had looked at her with recognition and then continued on their way. But she could remember the fear in her mother's voice, and she knew that she too was supposed to be afraid.

The next morning she had forgotten all about what had happened in the middle of the night, but when she put on her jacket to go out and explore, her father stopped her. Looking very serious, he told her that she had to stay right by their little cottage. He didn't tell her that he knew she had been in the forest, for he had learned it was best never to talk about such things. No matter how much she cried and argued with him, he wouldn't budge. But she knew that she needed to keep her connection with the forest of Aliveness, so she waited until her parents were distracted, and then she quickly slipped away to the secret garden, through the hidden doorway, and into the safety of the forest.

She still felt the joy of connecting with the birds and the flowers, with the sunlight as it filtered through the trees, and with the wind as it played in the grass, but somehow it was different. She didn't feel it all quite as deeply as she used to. One day she was startled by a loud and unfamiliar sound, and suddenly she remembered what her mother had said about the creatures in the forest—that they were not safe. Her breath became shallow, and her belly tightened, for she was sure it was a lion, tiger, or bear coming to get her. She ran back through the hidden doorway and into the cottage, where she locked her bedroom door and hid under her bed.

The memories of being completely connected to life began to fade as the thoughts in Rose's head became stronger, especially the ones telling her that she should be afraid of life because it could hurt her. Without her even noticing it, the free-flowing aliveness in her body began to dim. Much to her dismay, when Rose did find the courage to go out into the forest, she discovered that it was becoming harder and harder to squeeze herself through the hidden doorway. And when she did, rather than being open to the Magical Forest, she was on guard because she now had to watch out for the lions, tigers, and bears.

One evening, after hearing another scary sound in the forest and running back to her bedroom, she finally decided that it was time to be done with such childish things as secret gardens, hidden doorways, and magical forests. At first she felt great relief. She had become so confused and frightened that she began to feel safe and at home behind the walls of the village of Mind. Her parents lived here too, and because they were adults, they must know what was true. They didn't visit the Magical Forest at all. Everyone else she saw seemed to feel that the village was their home, so she figured it must be hers too. And all that nonsense about trusting life and feeling like everything was her friend was just her childish imagination, and she was too big for that now.

So Rose settled into the rhythm of life in the village of Mind, and even though it didn't truly feel like her home, she became fascinated with it. She was sent to a thing called school, and she was enthralled. She began to make sense of the squiggles in things called books, and much to her amazement she found some fairy tales about the Magical Forest! It was both wonderful and painful to revisit the memories of the place where she had been so happy and at home. Though she felt a twinge of homesickness as she remembered the forest, she would remind herself that she was being childish. She would then bury that feeling deep inside her, for she had learned in the village that feelings are not okay. Then she would remind herself, "I like being involved in all the thoughts in my head."

Her natural curiosity pulled her into exploring the maze of the village of Mind, and while following little, crooked alleys deep into its dark corners, Rose would sometimes get very lost. But she always seemed to be able to find her way back to the central square in the heart of the village. This was where she felt the happiest, for almost every day a market was held there. There were as many varieties of things as there had been birds, and trees, and flowers in the Magical Forest. She loved the swirl of color, the sounds of the musicians, and the wonderful smells of delicious food cooking.

She would still visit the secret garden at times, but she could no longer get through the door to the forest. Because the gates into the village were always locked and guarded, she was now completely caught in the village of Mind. One day, much to her despair, she could no longer find the secret garden. And eventually, as more and more thoughts filled her head, she found herself forgetting about the secret garden, the hidden doorway, and even the Magical Forest.

As she lost her connection with the aliveness of the forest, she found the maze of the village of Mind more and more fascinating. Gradually her head became completely filled with thoughts, and Rose spent more and more time thinking about life rather than truly experiencing it.

One day while exploring the furthest reaches of the village, she comes across a little hill. She is very happy because the rest of the village is mostly flat, so she has never gotten a chance to look at it all at the same time. This hill is barely high enough to allow her to see over the roof-tops, but as she sits there quietly drinking in the browns and reds and golds of the roof tiles, she is startled out of her reverie. She notices something that she hasn't recognized before—there are no trees in the village! Along with that realization, a faint memory of the Forest of Aliveness comes to her. Then a thought that almost stops her breath comes flooding in: "I have never noticed that not only are there no trees, but there are also no flowers or butterflies or even spiders (and definitely no slugs)!"

Rushing down the hill, she sees a little old lady carrying a basket of vegetables from the market-place. She asks her, "Why are there no trees?" Rose notices a glint of fear in the old woman's eyes. "Those things are of the world outside the village. We don't want to have anything to do with that. It is scary out there." At these words, a feeling of loss seeps into Rose's belly. It soon passes, however, as life continues in the vil-lage of Mind and she becomes entwined in her thoughts once again.

Late one afternoon, feeling a little lonely hang-ing out at the village square, Rose realizes that everybody she sees seems very intent on getting someplace else. The principal of her school stops to talk, but she notices that he is not really there with her. She then realizes that this is what happens with most people who stop to talk with her. They seem distracted and very rarely look into her eyes.

Another memory of the Magical Forest of Aliveness floats into her mind, and she remembers what it was like to be there—to be open to life, to feel the trees, to be moved by the stars, to play in the rivers, and to be held by the Earth. In a moment of clarity, she suddenly understands that in the Magical Forest she truly *saw* life as it unfolded around her and that she was also *seen* by everything. This epiphany brings forth the feeling of belonging she knew so well in the forest. As this wonderful memory begins to fade, she realizes that she feels the opposite in the village. Instead of a sense of belonging she is experiencing a sense of being alone.

She feels even lonelier than before, and an inner knowing tells her that the people of Mind are also feeling lonely and disconnected. It never used to seem that way to her because everyone appeared so purposeful, but now that she is growing up, she can see that they all feel half alive. For a moment she is overtaken by despair, but she has learned well in the village of Mind how to hold her breath and tighten her body to keep her feelings at bay.

The Dungeon

One morning, as she is talking with her friends at the well by the village square, Rose starts listening to the music coming from the hidden loudspeakers that are everywhere in the village. She has become so used to it that she very rarely hears it anymore. But today, in the crisp newness of the morning, she hears it as if for the first time, and she recognizes that very faint messages are being chanted within the music. She asks her friends if they hear the messages too, and they look at her as if she is crazy.

True, the words are so soft that she can barely hear them, but they are strangely familiar. The voices say: "You have to *do* life. And you have to

13

do it right. You have to figure it out and stay in control. Life cannot be trusted. When you *do it right* everything will be okay. If you don't *do it right*, the lions and tigers and bears will come and get you. So you must try to be the best. You are the best. No! You are not. You are less than everybody else. In fact, you are wrong. You are selfish. You are bad. You are all alone." In that moment, Rose realizes that she believes if she doesn't *do* life right, something terrible will happen. Perhaps she will be taken away and locked in the dungeons that she hears exist underground at the center of the village! She shivers in fear, for she doesn't believe she could exist in the darkness and isolation of the dungeons.

Turning her attention again to the words in the music, she notices that the voices are not only coming from the loudspeakers; they also live inside her head, and they have become stronger the longer she has lived in the village of Mind. With new clarity, she realizes that all these voices of control are there to keep her feelings at bay—especially the deep fear of life. This realization is so startling that she wants to stand up and shout to her friends: "That is what the lions and tigers and bears are all about! This is what my mother was talking about late that night—that you must be afraid of them because they represent the feelings we all have but don't know how to be with—fear, sadness, irritation, envy, anger, shame, jealousy, loneliness, despair, rage, unworthiness, terror, and even exuberance and silliness. But she suspects that her friends wouldn't understand, so she keeps this realization to herself.

For a moment it makes sense to her that feelings are a natural part of life, that everybody has them, and that most people don't like to acknowledge that. Everybody learned, just as she did, to hold their breath, tighten their bodies, and deny those feelings. She can see that all this trying to *do* life and *do it right* to free themselves from being overtaken by their feelings has never really worked. At that moment a volcano of feelings begins to erupt from within her, and almost immediately, since feelings are not accepted in the village, the police grab her and take her into the underground dungeons.

This first time in the dungeon is overwhelming. It is dark and damp, and Rose feels very alone. She doesn't know how long she will be there or even why she is there, but she feels miserable and very scared. Then an even worse feeling takes over—that she is there because she has done something wrong—and she curls up in a ball in the corner of the dungeon and cries and cries and cries.

When she decides to sit up again, without even understanding how or why, all of a sudden she is out of the dungeon, sitting again by the well. The experience of being lost in the deep feelings that got her thrown into the dungeon is scary, and it is even scarier that she doesn't know how to stop those feelings. Then faintly she begins to hear the voices of control and shame inside her, and she decides that if she just follows their lead—if she just *does life right* and stays in control—then she will be safe and won't ever have to go back into the dungeon again.

This works for awhile, but as Rose becomes a teenager, her feelings seem to take on a life of their own. One moment she's ecstatically happy over a new bracelet, then in a rage the next because her parents have grounded her. When she finds herself in the dungeon again, she experiences the desolation of being taken over by her feelings and the despair of not knowing how to stop them. One day, after a particularly difficult visit to the dungeon, her favorite aunt visits her there, and just seeing the love in her eyes releases Rose from all of the struggle she has been experiencing. Rather than feeling tight and disconnected, she begins to feel light and spacious as her heart begins to open again. In a flash she finds herself out of the dungeon and back into the imagined safety of the village.

But the memory of the dungeon stays with her and, rather than trusting the love she saw in her aunt's eyes, she focuses on her fear of the dungeon. She desperately tries to stop her feelings, and for awhile she figures out that if she just thinks positive thoughts and is really, really good, then the feelings will go away and she won't ever have to go to the dungeon again. But alas, the more she fights her feelings, the stronger they seem to become and the more she visits the dungeon. Her best friend tells her she likes someone else more, and back in the dungeon she goes. Her father comes home one night after drinking with his buddies and says mean and scary things to her, and there she is in the dungeon again.

All is not lost, however, for she discovers that if she stops by the corner bakery and buys lots of pastries to eat, she can numb herself out, and this will stop all the deep feelings that she doesn't know what to do with—at least for awhile. But they always come back again.

She sees that other people in the village are numbing themselves out too. Some of them stay up all night on the Internet or spend a lot of time at the local bar like her father or shopping like her mother, or they simply stay very busy, but she can see that these things don't really work. They also seem to be trying to get these activities under control, but Rose sees that their efforts are backfiring. As soon as they conquer one compulsion, another takes its place, like when her mother started eating a lot more when she stopped shopping as much. Rose sees that this is exactly what she is doing too, trying to numb herself with food and then trying to control her urge to overeat. A wave of self-judgment washes over her. "Why can't I control myself?" Then despair takes over. "It doesn't seem like there is any way out of this!" And back to the dungeon she goes.

The Tower

One day, feeling very sad, alone, and frustrated at being in the dungeon yet again, Rose thinks, "Well, since I seem to come here a lot, why don't I begin to explore this place?" It is so dark that she can't really see anything, so she decides to get to know it through touch, exploring all its nooks and crannies with her hands. As her curiosity becomes stronger than her fear of the dungeon, she notices something for the first time. A faint light is coming out of the rocks in the walls, and she feels warmth coming from this light that dispels some of the cold and damp of the dungeon.

Then she notices that the rocks in one part of the dungeon are radiating more light than anywhere else. As she begins to explore the pattern of the light in this area, it reveals itself as the outline of what looks like a doorway, and when she firmly pushes in just the right places, the rocks begin to move. Much to her amazement, they swing back and reveal a small, dark room. She feels a little thrill of discovery and immediately goes about exploring this new place.

Inside the room, her hands discover the cold metal of a spiral staircase. It is too dark to see where it goes. Nonetheless, she feels great excitement, and also some fear, as she begins to climb into unfamiliar territory. For a moment she looks back at the familiar dungeon with a little longing, but the urge to explore is stronger than her fear. As she climbs the stairs, she realizes that this is the tower she has seen as she explored the village, but has never been able to find the path leading into it. The higher she goes, the stronger the light gets and the lighter her heart becomes. At the very top, she discovers a room filled with windows, and her heart is overjoyed at the light flooding in.

She is drawn over to the closest window, and for the first time since she was little, she sees beyond the walls of the village of Mind, and there before her is the Magical Forest of Aliveness. Rose is filled with joy. With a clarity that she hasn't felt in years, she understands that early in her life she was able to get beyond the walls of Mind, through the hidden doorway in the secret garden and into the forest, where she was connected to herself and to life. Then, as she was taught to be afraid of life and especially of her feelings, she too, like almost everybody else, got caught behind the walls of the village of Mind.

As she looks down into the village with the imposing wall all around it, she recognizes that almost everybody there has become walled off from the experience of being truly alive. With deepening awareness, she sees that even though the walls of the village promise safety, it is a false promise because the truest safety she has known has come from being open to life. She now understands that this is what her time in the Magical Forest was all about. It reminded her of her true home, which is *being fully alive in this moment*. Looking out from the tower, she knows that this is the only moment that matters, and it is the doorway into the Magical Forest of Aliveness—no matter where she is, no matter what is happening.

From her new vantage point, Rose is also able to see that almost everybody in the village tumbles from one thought to another all day long, creating stories in their heads made out of beliefs that come from the loudspeakers. She realizes that they are caught in ideas *about* life rather than being open *to* life. She remembers something that the twinkly-eyed man who sells hot dogs by the well once said: "People have around 65,000 thoughts a day, and most of them are repeats from the day before!" At the time she thought he was kind of weird and didn't pay much attention to him, but now she finally understands what he was talking about. "Wow," she says to herself. "Most people live inside the walls of a 'Mind-made-me' rather than being present to life!"

For a few moments, it is almost as if she can hear all the thoughts going through the minds of the people she sees moving to and fro in the village below her. She understands now that their minds are a lot like hers. They struggle with almost everything, from the shape of their bodies to whether they are good enough or smart enough or likable enough. With a deep sadness, she recognizes that they are all experiencing the same thing she is - that most of the stories in their heads come from the idea that who they are is not okay. They are constantly trying to get away from what they don't like and to go to what they do like, and it is all based on the belief that this moment is not enough.

She realizes that this struggling with life is what keeps everyone from being fully alive. A wave of fury washes over her. "I want to get out of this village of Mind! I want to get out of this endless place of struggle!" With a passion she hasn't felt in a long time, she runs down the stairs, rushes out into the village, and makes her way to the main gate. Of course it is locked, just as it has been every day of her life. She pounds on the sturdy barrier with all her might only to bloody her hands, and soon the police come and take her back to the dungeon.

This time, the curiosity that woke up inside her in the tower comes into play, and rather than resisting the dungeon, Rose begins to explore it. Quickly she sees the light emanating from the rocks and remembers the doorway into the tower, and up she goes again into the light-filled room. As she looks out over the Magical Forest of Aliveness, she notices for the first time that the village of Mind is actually in the middle of the forest and that it only appears to be separate. In a flash of insight, she understands that the forest and the village are both important parts of life—that every cell, animal, plant, rock, person, fungus, cloud, dewdrop, winter storm, shaft of sunlight and even the village of Mind itself are integral parts of the whole.

But the moment passes, and Rose still wants to break free of the confines of mind. She is smarter this time. She doesn't rush the walls. Instead, she plans a prison break. She secretly buys a pick and shovel, and in the middle of a very dark moonless night, she digs a tunnel under the wall. Oh, the joy of that moment when she breaks through the last bit of dirt and stands close once again to the Magical Forest of Aliveness. She looks across the field between the village and the forest, and even though she is very excited, she is also afraid. She hasn't been truly open to life in a long, long time.

What she doesn't realize is that whenever anyone breaks out of the prison of mind, an invisible tether tied around her ankle activates as soon as she gets beyond the wall of the village. After Rose enjoys a few breathtaking and joyous moments of being truly open to life, with no warning the tether tugs on her, pulling her instantly back through the tunnel and into the walled-off confines of Mind. Despair wells up inside her, but it is also accompanied by something that confuses her—fear. "Why am I afraid to be free?" she asks herself. Then the realization dawns that the last time she truly opened to life was when she was very young. She got scared out of it by her parents and by the subliminal messages broadcasting all across the village. As this fear now wells up, back into the dungeon she goes.

This time it takes a bit longer to remember the tower because the voices in her mind are saying, "You can't trust life. You should never have tried a prison break because the forest of Aliveness is not safe. The only safety is in staying in control."

But now another voice calls to her too, saying, "It is okay to be open to life. In fact, it is the safest thing you will ever know. Open right now, even here in the dungeon. For right now, *this is life*, and it's okay! There is no need to resist anything. You are not here because you have done something wrong or because something wrong was done to you. And your suffering is not what it looks like on the surface. The treasures of awakening back into life are hidden in the places inside you that you are most afraid to be with. As you learn how to be with them, each will reveal a treasure to you. So right now open to this dungeon. It is truly the safest thing you will ever do."

The old voices of resistance try to drown out this new one. But she remembers the spacious joy she felt in the room at the top of the tower. She also notices how the old thoughts are contracting her into fear, taking her deeper into the dungeon. So she summons her courage and cautiously makes her way back up the staircase, settling herself by the windows.

As Rose sits quietly watching the forest, she begins to *feel* it again. It's almost as if the forest is speaking to her, telling her that life knows what it is doing—that spring unfolds out of winter naturally without her needing to do anything about it; that the stars dance through the night sky in breathtaking precision. She remembers something she learned in school—that she started as one tiny, microscopic cell, and now she is made out of 100 trillion cells, and they all work together without a single thought from her. "Wow," Rose says to herself. "Life is orchestrated by an Intelligence that is way beyond anything I can even comprehend, let alone control."

With this realization, her body naturally begins

to breathe more easily, and as laughter bubbles up from within her, she recognizes that life is smarter than she is. It is safe to open to it all; to open to life is to trust life, and to trust life is to experience herself as an integral part of this great river of creativity that is life.

Her gaze shifts to the village life beneath her. She sees that everybody is destined to be born with a connection to the Magical Forest of Aliveness, where they trust themselves and trust life, and then to leave this trust for the illusion of control that is the hallmark of the village of Mind. She realizes that all the people she sees hurrying from here to there at one time experienced how to *be* life, even though now are lost in *doing* life.

As she looks more closely, she notices something that was hard to see when she didn't have access to the tower: everybody in the village has clouds around their heads. They are lost in stories in their minds too. With an ache in her heart, she understands that even though she felt she was the only one constantly being sent to the dungeon, the fact is that everybody spends time there, and the causes are many: the nights when they wake up afraid they won't have enough money to make ends meet; the days at work when anger at their boss overtakes them; the heart-breaking loneliness after the breakup of a relationship; and the cruel self-judgment that keeps them feeling isolated and alone.

From her vantage point high in the tower, she also sees that the endless game of control and shame will never heal these deep feelings. The peace that everyone longs for comes when they can simply accept themselves as they are and relearn how to trust life.

So she rushes down out of the tower and runs around to everybody, wanting to bring them the good news. "You are caught in your mind. Let go. The walls of Mind are keeping you imprisoned. Open them and let life in, and everything will flow as it needs to." Well, this is the last thing the people living in the village of Mind want to hear. They shout back at her, "If we don't stay inside the walls of Mind, then either nothing will happen, or something bad will happen. There are lions, tigers, and bears right outside the walls of the village, and we must keep busy and stay in control to keep them at bay." They call the police, and back to the dungeon Rose goes.

Opening of the Heart

This time her dungeon visit is completely different. Instead of fearful messages, Rose hears music that sounds like a choir of angels, and the voices are singing, "Everybody is exactly where they need to be on this great journey of life. You don't need to fix them or judge them or change them. All they need from you is for you to see them without needing them to be any different."

As she hears this truth, Rose finds herself immediately in the room at the top of the tower without even needing to climb the stairs. This time when she looks down and sees all the people rushing around, a warm glow radiates from her chest, and she begins to see them through the eyes of her own heart. She understands that, yes, they are all caught up in "doing" life, but they are exactly where they need to be in their journey through life.

She also sees that they are doing their absolute best with what they have been given—with the kind of parents they had, the kind of health, the kind of mind, the kind of emotional makeup, and the kind of environment. She can even see that this is true about herself.

Rose acknowledges, however, that often she has seen the people in her life through the eyes of judgment. She is astounded to see how much she has judged and she begins to judge her judgment, but she recognizes that all this does is close her heart and she very quickly lets go of judging herself. For she can see that she too has been doing the best she could do with what she has been given by life. She can also see that everybody in the village is caught in judgment, both of themselves and of others, far away from the healing of their own hearts.

She then remembers her epiphany in the dungeon—that what these people most need from her is her undivided, accepting attention. But her mind immediately thinks of the person she most dislikes in the village. What comes right after that is the person she most fears, and finally another for whom she feels sorry. "How can I possibly give these people my full attention and acceptance?" cries her mind. With a sudden flash of awareness, she recognizes that everybody in the village whom she disliked or judged or was afraid of was just reminding her of parts of herself that she hasn't yet learned to love!

She remembers her next door neighbor Margaret who she used to judge harshly for how talkative she was. Now Rose understands that Margaret was reminding her of all the times in her life she felt she had talked too much and judged herself harshly too. Then, one day, when she began to see how the talkative one inside of her was just trying to cover over her anxiety, she found she wasn't very judgmental about this part of herself any more. And even more amazing, as she accepted her talkative one she didn't feel the need to talk so much!

She realizes that the most important work of her life is to recognize, love, and include every single part of herself, for she is a community just like the village is a community, and just like the forest is too. Her heart begins to glow as she sees that every part of her is necessary in the wholeness of herself. It is such an astonishing realization. She finally understands that the healing she has longed for isn't about getting rid of the parts of herself that she doesn't like. It is about including them in her heart.

Rose then invents a new game in which she spends a long time in the tower observing the people going about their lives in the village below, watching for the ones she reacts to. Whenever she sees someone who causes her to tighten inside, she turns her attention to herself, meeting whatever is arising inside her with understanding and mercy. It's a most enjoyable game!

The next time Rose goes down into the village she is much more present to everything that is happening. As she is walking to the village square, from behind her she hears a voice call her name. As she turns around, her whole body immediately contracts, for there in front of her is Billy, her first love, and their relationship had ended in deep pain. When he left her for her best friend, he told her that she was stupid, selfish and ugly. These were her greatest fears about herself, so she had completely believed what he said. After that she drew herself into a cocoon of self judgment that stayed with her for years.

Whenever she saw him, these old judgments would rush into her mind and cause her to freeze, or she would hate him with a vengeance. And now with him standing in front of her, both of these come rushing through her. Everything inside her tightens, and she finds herself immediately back in the dungeon.

This time, enough light is emanating from the rocks that she can see a brass placard bolted into the wall that says "Resistance Only Increases Suffering." At first she finds this intimidating, but then she smiles as she recognizes the truth of this statement—that resisting her feelings never got her where she wanted to be. Now it makes sense that what pulled her back over and over again into the dungeon wasn't all the deep and uncomfortable feelings inside her. *It was her resistance to them*!

Immediately she is back in the village, standing in front of Billy and everything changes. Rather than getting lost in her reactions, she turns her attention inside of herself and, with great curiosity, sees what she is feeling. As she meets these feelings with understanding and mercy, they begin to dissipate and she finds herself able to just be with Billy without judgment or fear.

Such joy!

Now her life in the village becomes an amazing adventure. She knows there are no ordinary moments, and definitely no ordinary experiences. Rather than resisting life, she sees every experience either as an invitation to be fully present to life or as an invitation to see the feelings she has been running away from and the beliefs that have kept them frozen inside her. So every day is a new adventure, with life bringing her the experiences she needs in order to heal.

For the first time, Rose truly understands what forgiveness is about. It isn't about saying, "You have done me wrong, and I am now letting you off the hook." Forgiveness is letting things be as they have been, as they are, and as they will be—so *she lets herself off the hook*! She sees that forgiveness isn't about the other person as much as it is about unhooking herself from the hardness that non-forgiveness brings into her life. Not that she should condone a cruel or hurtful action, but she can forgive the person, and in that forgiveness she becomes free. She also realizes she doesn't have to let difficult people back into her life, but she can let them into her heart.

As she feels the release of forgiving the people who have deeply challenged her, for the first time she truly forgives herself. Yes, she has made many mistakes, but that is part of the job description of being a human being. It finally makes sense to her that her perfection includes her imperfection! The deep self-judgment that has been there since thoughts first began to fill her head softens dramatically—even the core belief that somehow she is bad and wrong. A warm glow in her chest begins to expand and fill her whole body.

With a sigh of relief, she concludes that whenever the judging voice shows up in her head, she doesn't have to believe what it is saying. Instead she can see it as a call for kindness. And the more her mind drops into her heart, the more she will be able to simply be with her life as it is happening, giving whatever is showing up her full attention. Why, already her breathing isn't anywhere near as shallow as it used to be, and she is experiencing more moments of something she hasn't felt in a long time—joy!

Everybody she comes across now as she walks through the village either opens her heart or gives her the opportunity to open her heart to herself. When she stops to talk to people, her ability to be fully present to them feels wonderful. With great joy she notices that people light up when she is fully there with them, and then they take that light of presence to the next person they meet, and they too light up. "This is how the world heals," her awareness says. "People who can truly be present and available to whatever is happening right now become an invitation to others to open again to life."

As she walks through the village seeing everything through the eyes of compassion, much to her amazement, trees begin to appear in the village, and for the first time in a very long while she hears the trill of a bird. When she looks down, a line of ants is marching over her foot, and she is filled with an indescribable happiness. Even when she comes across a spider spinning its web, rather than being afraid of it as she would have been in the past, she is amazed by its beauty and creativity.

Memories of the forest of Aliveness begin to fill her awareness. "I knew this way of being with life when I was very young, and then I fell asleep," she reflects. "I was like Sleeping Beauty—I pricked my finger on the spindle of fear and got lost in my mind!" At the same time, she feels a little afraid, because it was one thing to look at the Magical Forest of Aliveness from the vantage point of the tower, and another to have it begin to show up in the village of Mind.

She still has moments of believing the old voices in the music that chant, "Control, control, control. The only safety is in control." But now she has experienced too much of the free-flowing aliveness and heart energy that come from opening to life to close back down again into fear. So even though these old voices bring up deep feelings that can throw her back into the dungeon for short periods, she now knows that the dungeon is where she can find the doorway to the tower. Whenever she goes for a visit, there is always something new to be learned. The quiet music of the rocks more easily soothes the scared and angry voices within her, and as she is touched by the wisdom of her heart, Rose truly begins to know that she is okay, that life is okay, and that everything is going to be okay.

Even as the village of Mind slowly fills with the magic of the forest of Aliveness, at times the old feelings start to take over again. But then she remembers that the village of Mind is based on resistance, and as she includes rather than resists what she is experiencing, allowing her feelings to pass through her rather than getting lost in them, she rarely goes to the dungeon anymore. In fact, she discovers a hidden pathway in the village that takes her right to the tower, bypassing the dungeon altogether!

The Magical Forest

One day, walking down the street that borders the outer wall of the village, Rose is surprised to see that the gate is partially open and that no guards are around. She somehow knows that because she has been willing to see with great kindness all the parts of herself, the locked gate of her mind is open again to life. With excitement, but also with some fear, she steps through the gate and into the Magical Forest of Aliveness. She looks down and is surprised to see that there is no tether tied to her ankle anymore, and suddenly it is a bit scary to be this free. So she sits down on a bench against the wall and looks out across the field between the walls of the village and the edge of the Magical Forest which is large enough for her to feel comfortable just watching and listening.

Drinking it all in, Rose begins to focus on an oak tree at the edge of the forest, and she has an amazing experience. Rather than just seeing it, she *feels* it! She recalls that when she used to play in the forest when she was very young, this is how she experienced life—she didn't think about it—she felt it! As she opens to feeling the tree, she experiences it not as a separate object but as nothing less than life expressing itself, and she realizes that it took all the creativity that has ever unfolded on this planet to bring forth this amazing creation in front of her.

She observes how the tree both receives from life and gives back. It receives the sun, the rain, the minerals from the ground, and even the bees that pollinate its flowers and the birds that spread its seeds. At the same time it gives bountiful blessings to life, feeding the birds and the bees with its flowers and fruits and continuing life through its seeds.

When she takes her next breath, she realizes that she is breathing in the gift of oxygen that the trees before her just breathed out. As she breathes out, she knows that they receive her carbon dioxide as a blessing. Tears begin to flow, for she finally sees *herself* as a part of the great circle of giving and receiving that is life. She sees that everything is one interconnected web and everything needs everything else in order to exist! She is not separate from this tree. She too is an integral and necessary part of life. She too belongs.

Rose stays on that bench long enough and becomes quiet enough that she catches glimpses of the lions, tigers, and bears as they move through the forest. A bear comes to the very edge of the woods and looks deeply into her eyes from across the field, and she feels no fear for she recognizes it as the symbol of the deep feelings that are a part of being human. She knows that as she learns to stay open to all the lions, tigers, and bears within her rather than running away from them or trying to get rid of them, they will simply pass through like the bear, blessing her with their presence.

After many visits to the bench, Rose begins to feel pulled to explore the Magical Forest. With great anticipation, but also with the old fears rumbling through her belly, she enters this sacred land. Immediately upon being enfolded by its presence, a deep sense of peace pervades her. Rather than being afraid, she begins to feel a childlike sense of wonder. Everything is a feast for her senses—the sights, the sounds, the smells. "Life is so amazing!" she says to herself. "I am finally awake to life again: awake to the wonder, the mystery, and the newness of every moment and every thing!"

The Clearing

As she feels her aliveness awakening, it almost becomes too much, for she hasn't been this open to life since she was a child. Then she comes to a clearing in the forest beside a musical brook, and with relief she lies down on the carpet of green. All the tension that was being held in her body relaxes, and she melts into being held by the Earth. Rose feels her breath and lets go to it, riding this mother rhythm of life. She opens deeply enough that she allows herself to be breathed by life.

Her attention then comes fully into her body, and she can feel that the more she relaxes, the more energy flows freely through every part of her. The more she lets go, the more vibrant this aliveness becomes, until her body is glowing from head to foot. "I never knew that there was such bliss in simply being present to my body," she says to herself. She notices that as soon as she thinks just a little bit about what is happening, the free-flowing aliveness dims a bit, but as soon as she brings her attention back fully into her body, it opens again. This sense of aliveness now begins to expand beyond her body, and she realizes with delight that everything in that clearing—the dirt, the rocks, the grass and flowers, the sunlight, the trees, the birds and the bees—are also made out of the same energy of aliveness.

She finally experiences in the very cells of her being what she saw from the tower—that she is connected to everything, and everything is connected to her. As she looks at the forest around her and feels the Earth beneath her and listens to the music of the brook, she feels the Intelligence in every single molecule of every single thing that makes up the clearing. And she understands at a deeper level that this Intelligence knows what it is doing and that it is safe to open to it.

With a flash of insight, Rose sees that her body too is this field of Intelligence. But then comes a moment of sadness, for she realizes she had always seen it as an object that she needed to do something with—make it better or different than what it was—so she had never truly *listened* to it. She hugs herself with the deepest love she has ever known. "My body is my friend," she says with tears rolling down her cheeks. "It is a wise, wise friend, and as I listen to it, it will guide me unfailingly along my path of life."

As she sits up, everything has changed in her perception. She can now see a faint halo of light radiating from everything. She had read in her science book that life was made out of light, but it was just too big of a thought for her. Now she can feel it and see it, and even understand that this was what all the halo business was about. People who had opened to life, truly opened, were often painted with halos around their heads. This was because when they opened and recognized the truth of light, they became radiant! Right now she can feel that radiance in every cell of her being, and the word that comes closest to what she is experiencing is *delight*. As this word rolls through her mind and heart, she starts to laugh. "De-light. Of the light!—Of course, 'of the light!'"

As she opens to the light radiating from everything in this beautiful clearing, another realization resonates to her core—that the activity of this light is Love. Her eyes begin to fill with tears of gratitude and they run in little rivulets down her cheeks. "This is the Love that is spoken about at the heart of every religion," says the voice of truth inside her. For the first time she allows herself to be deeply and fully touched, right there in that clearing, by the Love radiating from every particle of life.

The experience of being truly seen and loved fills her with its healing balm, and she recognizes that she has deeply longed for this her whole life. The voice of truth speaks again. "This Love is the essence at the heart of life, and you are not alone." "I am not alone," sing the very cells of her being. "I am not alone! And whenever I forget this, all I need to do is ask Love for help, for it is always with me, even when I doubt that this is so." These realizations open Rose so deeply that her breath flows freely through her, going all the way down into the center of her belly, and she knows that she can do this whenever she finds herself struggling. Through her breath she can ground herself into her body and into this moment where Love dwells.

Her attention is then drawn over to her right, where she sees a beautiful tree filled with flowers. With joy she thinks, "My life is like that tree! Powerful forces birthed me out of Mystery and rooted me in the soil of life. And just like a tree, they 'grew' me through the many and varied experiences of my life. I thought I was doing it all, that I was in charge, but all along the way I was being lived by life. Now that I am again opening into life, it is my time to flower and fruit. I am being ripened by life into the fruit of a mature human being—an alive, loving, present-moment awareness!"

Rose stays in the clearing as the sunlight fades and the stars begin to appear. As darkness envelopes the forest, she sees the subtle light radiating from everything, and she understands that even in the darkest times of her life, she was not separate from the Light and Love at the heart of Life itself.

She lies down in the soft grass and continues breathing all the way down into her belly. She's not sure how long she's been lying there, when suddenly she hears a crashing sound in the forest, and her fear of life starts to take over again.

As she sits up, her whole body begins to freeze. She knows it is one of the wild creatures of her deep feelings that is coming to the clearing to devour her. It was one thing to recognize from a distance that her feelings are nothing to be afraid of, but this is entirely different.

As Rose grapples with a fear so great she can hardly take a breath, a giant bear steps out into the clearing. But instead of charging her, it stands quietly, deeply looking into her eyes. Much to her amazement, Rose's belly begins to soften and her breath slows. For the first time in her life, she discovers that it is truly okay to feel this deep fear! With a bit of sadness, she sees that she has been thoroughly trained to do the opposite with all her feelings. She tried to stop them and stuff them, but they just turned into something else or they leaked out around the edges of her control.

Looking deeply into the bear's eyes, she remembers what she saw so clearly in the tower—that there is nothing wrong with any of her feelings. With deep gratitude, she recognizes that there is nothing inside her to be ashamed or afraid of. Feelings are just a part of the flow of energy that is life. She knows that the full range of feelings available to a human being is inside her, and in her willingness to feel them, whatever they may be, and listen to the stories that go along with them, she won't get lost in them.

As her attention comes back to her body, she notices that the knot of fear in her belly hasn't yet fully let go. She looks again at the bear and realizes that this is just trapped energy inside her that she is calling fear, and it is frozen there through her resistance to it. Rose is immediately reassured and becomes curious about what this energy in her body is like. As she gives it her accepting attention, this tightly held knot begins to open and the energy that was bound there is released back into the free-flowing aliveness of her body. The joy of simply experiencing a feeling without getting caught up in it or running away from it arises now within her, replacing all her fear.

"I don't need to run away from the lions, tigers, and bears inside me," she says to the bear. "All the parts of me I have hated and feared are just asking for a hug. This is what they have longed for my whole life—for me to not resist them, ignore them, or fix them. As I open to these parts of me, they will no longer seduce me into struggle, cutting me off from the joy of being fully present to life."

"But I won't always know what I am feeling," she tells the bear. "What do I do then?" As Rose looks into the liquid brown aliveness in the bear's eyes, he says, "You are ready to know one of the most important things you can learn on the journey back to life. You can ask life for clarity but not in the old way you have learned of asking questions. Instead, ask a question, and then let it go. When you understand that the true power of a question is the question itself, you will understand that when you ask a question without looking for an answer you are signaling the Intelligence at the heart of life that you are ready to listen. And life will live the answer through you in its time and in its way."

Rose feels the truth of what he is inviting her into, and she asks, "What question would I ask when I am unsure about what I am feeling?" The bear responds, "First ask, 'What am I experiencing, right now?' and bring your attention into your body, for all your feelings also show up as sensations. You may notice a lump in your throat or a fist in your solar plexus or overall agitation. Let your attention rest in a pocket of sensations and the feelings that are fueling those sensations will reveal themselves over time. If nothing is clear, ask, 'What is asking to be seen?'

and let it go. Life will show you in its own way when you are ready."

The bear, recognizing her deepening awareness, makes a courtly bow and turns and walks back into the forest.

Rose lies down again, and through breathing deeply she lets go of any tension that is left in her body, and again she allows herself to be held by the Earth. Right there in the middle of the Magical Forest of Aliveness, under a canopy of thousands and thousands of stars, she returns fully to the trust of her self and of life that is her birthright. As she watches the constellations dance around the North Star, every cell of her being begins to vibrate with joy. "I am being held by the Earth, and as the Earth holds me she is held by nothing but space!"

At that moment Rose's awareness expands so greatly that she experiences herself moving through vast oceans of space while she is being held by this precious blue-green jewel of a planet. She remembers something she had heard in school many years ago—that there are more stars than there are grains of sand on every beach of the Earth! She can see that right now, in that clearing, she is surrounded by stars. They are above her and below her, to the left of her and to the right. "I am a part of the immensity of the universe," says her awed awareness. "And it is a part of me!" She then slips into a deep and restful sleep.

At dawn she notices that she is feeling the pull of the village, and much to her amazement she doesn't feel grief about leaving this clearing. What the clearing showed her is the Light and Love at the heart of life, and that it is with her always—no matter where she is and no matter what is happening. It is her guide, her friend, and her lover and will be with her wherever she goes. The bear has shown her how to let her feelings move through her rather than holding onto them or resisting them, and he has taught her that she can ask life for clarity.

As Rose enters the forest canopy, she turns back to the clearing to bow in gratitude for all that she learned here, and then continues into the forest for the return journey to the village of Mind.

Return to the Village

As Rose gets closer to the village, she hesitates a little, for the fear that she will lose this connection with life begins to arise within her. "I just want the space and light of the clearing!" she exclaims. As fear gains a foothold in her mind, she becomes seduced into the thought that she can't *do* this awakening that life is offering her. She spirals down into self-judgment, listening to the voices that are saying not only that she can't *do* it, but that if she tries she won't be able to *do it right*. Noticing that her chest feels tight, she sits down on a moss-covered log and opens herself to long, slow, deep breaths, breathing in the breath of the forest.

Gradually her mind quiets, and the fear lets go. When she hears movement behind her, she turns without a tremor of fear and sees a stately lion with the most compassionate face she has ever seen. As they look into each other's eyes, the space between them and all around them becomes suffused with the energy she felt in the clearing, and the lion gives her another important realization. "The dream you are waking up from is the idea that you are the one that is *doing* your life. Feel this idea that you have to *do* your life and feel the tightness it brings. Now feel the opening and the trust of life you remembered in the clearing. This openness, this willingness to *allow* life rather than *doing* life connects you to your own deep wisdom that is a part of the Intelligence that animates all of life. *Allowing* life isn't about not doing anything. It is about not resisting life so your *doing* can arise from your own innate wisdom. This wisdom comes from the Intelligence that keeps the planets spinning and heals the cuts on your skin. It is always with you, and you can trust it."

Opening again into the spacious trust she connected with in the clearing, Rose's body relaxes. The lion then says, "In the tower you saw that one of the core stories you got lost in was that who you are and what your life is right now is not enough. It promises that the peace you long for will come when you 'get it together.' As long as you believe that, you will be caught in the game of struggle. Most people are caught by these judging thoughts, and it cuts them off from their heart."

The lion sees that she understands and continues, "One of the keys to releasing yourself from the constant struggle of the mind is to be able to see judgment, especially your self-judgment, and not be seduced into its game. The judger inside you contains not one iota of truth. I know it says many things that feel like they are true, but they aren't. Are you ready to see through its game and love yourself as you are? It takes courage to do this, but it is the core task given to you by life—to fully accept yourself as you are.

"You are not perfect. Nobody is. You have strengths and weaknesses, and you have been both skillful and unskillful. But there is nothing to judge. Your perfection includes your imperfection. Whenever you are caught in judgment you can ask life, 'Show me how to meet myself in my heart.' As you meet yourself with compassion you begin to recognize that underneath all the stories in your head your basic nature is goodness, and when you embrace yourself as you are, you naturally live from this compassion and become a healing force in the world."

As she takes in what the lion is saying, her heart opens to every single part of herself.

"Oh my," she says, her heart filled with laughter. "This means that I can be exactly who I am— all of me!" Looking into the lion's eyes, she is reminded of another thing the tower taught her. "As I spend time again in the village, I will of course make mistakes. But the fact is, with all the mis-takes I have made in my life, I have never really made a mistake because they were all a part of the dance of opening and closing that is life. Of course there are parts of me that need to mature, but instead of judging them, I will meet them with compassion."

With compassion filling her being, she remembers something she heard many years ago: "I am not okay, and you're not okay, and that is okay!" Again joy fills her whole body as her wisdom self speaks to her: "Sometimes the inhabitants of Mind, including me, are as nutty as a fruit-cake, but it is that very nuttiness that will grab my attention. This allows me to see clearly all the parts of me I haven't yet come to love and haven't yet woven into the wholeness of who I am. So, finally, it is okay to be authentically myself, and in this opening to life as it is and as I am, life can freely move through me!"

Rose now knows this is her task—to become fully herself. She has been given the gift of life because there is something that she can do that nobody else can. She feels willing to meet all of herself in her heart so that she can move through life in her authenticity. Just as the bear did, the lion bows to Rose, honoring that she now truly understands that she can love every part of her. She bows in return, knowing the wisdom she received from the lion will be with her always.

As Rose turns and makes her way to the village, she feels a warm glow in her heart and a deep sense of ease. Suddenly, a tiger jumps down from a tree limb above her and announces its presence with a roar. Even with all the trust of life that Rose has opened up to here in the Magical Forest, she trembles for a moment in the tiger's presence. But as her fear calms, she can hear the wisdom the tiger is here to impart. "I represent the deep challenges of your life, and I am your friend. If you don't fight me, I will bring you great gifts." Rose knows what the tiger is saying is true, for she can see that every challenge has brought her another step closer to her awakening. She feels a wave of gratitude for everything that has happened, even the visits to the dungeon, for they opened her to the awareness she experienced in the tower.

She remembers the phrase that came to her in one of her dungeon visits: "Right now, *this is life*, and it's okay!" Returning the tiger's gaze she says, "When I am feeling challenged by something, I don't need to resist. For it is life, and I can let it move through me, responding rather than reacting." The tiger nods in agreement. She then says with great passion, "It is safe to experience whatever I am experiencing! Suffering comes from resisting what is happening. Joy comes from opening to what is, no matter what." The smile in the tiger's eyes lights up its whole face. Laughter fills Rose's being. "It is all trustable," she says to the tiger. "That is what I didn't see. It may not always be likable, but it is trustable." She shouts for the pure joy of it. "I can trust my life. It is safe to open to it." As she starts to get carried away with elation, the tiger softly growls to focus her attention.

Rose turns and looks into the tiger's eyes and feels chills all over her body as she understands that she is ready to know something she has never allowed herself to know before. As she becomes still, the tiger speaks. "In order to become free from your 'Mind-made-me,' all you need to do is see it—watch it as it spins its stories inside your head. That is what your challenges are for. They are tailor-made to bring up the core beliefs you took on as a child.

"Some of the core beliefs that almost everybody takes on are: I am not good enough; life never works out for me; I must be in control; life is not safe; I need to be different from what I am; I am all alone. When these old beliefs come to the surface, instead of being afraid of your experience, you can trust it as a doorway. To walk through that doorway when your mind is filled with these old beliefs, you don't need to fix them, get rid of them, or even understand where they came from. Seeing them is enough. Simply by giving them the light of your attention, you transform them.

"So the operative word is *look*! When you are caught in an old belief that engenders fear, you don't need to fall into it. You can watch it operate inside you. Rather than saying 'I am afraid,' you can say, 'This is my story of fear.' The same is true for all the stories that fuel your anger, doubt, self-judgment, sadness, and even despair. These are all parts of your 'Mind-made me,' and as you watch them, rather than being lost in them, you can discover that who you are is not the same as the stories in your head. You are that which can see them.

"Every time you *relate to* the suffering inside you rather than getting lost in it, you help to heal the world, for at the core your suffering is the same suffering that all human beings experience. When you don't get hooked into it, it becomes possible for every human being you touch to get unhooked too."

Rose feels the truth of what the tiger is saying, but when she thinks about the suffering in the world, she is confused and says, "I see now that when I move from the truth that my challenges are for me, I am no longer a victim, so I can be with them in a fresh, spontaneous way. But how can I do this with all the suffering in the world? My heart breaks when I see the greed, fear, brutality, and starvation that are taking place all over our planet. What do I do about that? I want to help, but then I get overwhelmed. When I do try to help, it doesn't seem to be enough, or it is rejected."

"Yes, there is suffering in the world," says the tiger. "Everyone goes through it. If we look at it through the eyes of our conditioned self, we label it as something bad that must be changed. We then live from reaction, resisting it, judging it, trying to fix it or get rid of it. It takes a long while to see that when we fight anything, we empower it. When we are in that frame of mind, we also tend to see people as victims which disempowers them, freezing them into problem mode.

"We are all attuned to this. When somebody tries to rescue us, we tend to resist, hearing the message that we can't handle our lives or that there is something wrong with us. It is an entirely different experience when a person trusts that our suffering is a necessary part of our journey and that in the core of our being, we know our way through it. This empowers us to move out of victim mode and discover that the resources needed for our challenge are within us and always have been.

"This doesn't mean that we don't help others. If our help is called for and if we don't see them as victims, we are able to respond to the situation rather than reacting to it. Our response will then come from our deep center of wisdom, and our actions will bring forth harmony and healing in whatever way is most needed."

As she allows these truths into her being, she

feels certain that she will never be a victim of her life again. The tiger will show up as illness, loss, heartbreak, deep fear, and even death. But she now knows that these challenges are a part of life, just like winter. She sees that they will not come because she has done something wrong, because others have done something wrong, or because the powers that be fell asleep on the job. Each experience will either invite her into this moment where life is, or will show her which of her old beliefs are keeping her separate.

As Rose lets herself be open to her life—all of it, including the challenges—she recognizes that the Magical Forest has now moved her beyond the kind of mind she has lived in her whole life—the dualistic mind that labels things as *good* and *bad*, *right* and *wrong*. She sees now that contraction and spaciousness are just the opposite ends of the spectrum and that she can be open to both. With this understanding, she will no longer value one experience over another. Instead she can open to whatever life brings, right here, right now.

"This is what joy is all about!" she exclaims. "I thought I would only find the happiness I have been chasing my whole life when life was the way I wanted it. But life was always changing, and I could never hold onto the happiness I longed for. Joy comes from the ability to be with life as it is!" She can feel the truth of these words as they move through her mind and heart. "This is it! Right now, *this is it*. There's even a fierce tiger in front of me, and it's okay!" Rose bows to the tiger first—so accustomed is she to meeting these wild animals in the forest now—and she sees a glint of laughter in this fierce tiger's eyes as it bows in return and melts back into the forest.

The Field

It is only a short way to the village now, and as Rose comes to the field at the edge of the forest she stops, sits down, and looks across to the village of Mind where she had been so cut off from life. Much to her amazement, as she sees the village through the eyes of Light and Love, the wall around it gets smaller and smaller until it is no higher than a garden fence. She understands that this is happening because of the opening she experienced in the Magical Forest and that it is now safe to be curious about life.

She sees that she will be able to move more easily between the village of Mind and the Magical Forest of Aliveness, for they are both a part of this great mystery of life. Ever since she first saw the forest from the tower, she felt that all she wanted to do was leave the village of Mind behind and live in the forest forever, but she realizes now that one of the gifts she was given by life is her mind. It is an amazing and necessary tool for maneuvering though life, but it can also be an oppressive jailer. She can now see that it is full of conditioned beliefs and relies on conceptual knowledge for its truth. This reliance on knowledge takes her from the part of her that *knows* how to sense and feel life—the part of her that is connected to the wisdom at the heart of life.

Rose knows that it is her job to go back into the village of Mind and free up the parts of her that don't yet trust her knowing and that still struggle. Even though she sees the truth that being open to life is the safest and most joyous thing she can do, and she recognizes the power of allowing life to flow through her rather than trying to control it, there are still parts of her that don't know these truths.

She wonders how she can possibly invite the rest of the walls in her mind to dissolve so she can come back into the wonder and joy of being truly present. It was one thing to be able to trust it all while in the Magical Forest, but to do it in her daily life in the village of Mind feels a bit daunting. She then hears movement behind her as the lion, tiger, and bear come to be with her.

As they sit down beside her, she turns and looks into the bear's eyes, and remembers the wisdom that he had imparted to her—that it is okay to feel whatever she is feeling and she can be with her feelings so they can move through her rather than getting stuck inside her. Also she can ask questions of life without looking for an answer, and life will live the answer through her. As she looks into the lion's eyes, she recognizes that the core gift she can give to life is to meet herself—all of her—in her own heart and that there is nothing about her to be afraid or ashamed of. And as she looks into the tiger's eyes, she remembers that the challenges she will experience will always come with gifts and they are not here because she is doing something wrong or life is punishing her. A wave of gratitude for all these formerly scary creatures fills her and brings tears to her eyes.

With a full awareness of the wisdom each of these new friends has given her, Rose looks back at the village. As she does so, the word *surrender* begins to intrigue her. Whereas in the world of Mind it was quite an unwanted word—a word that meant giving up or letting life take over—Rose now understands its true meaning. It means partnership with the vast creative river called life, letting it lead the way. The wisdom voice within her speaks again: "There is nothing I need to figure out or solve. Life is a mystery. I can't control it, but I can open to it and engage with it as it is *right now.*"

As she starts to get up to walk toward the village, her old fears suddenly rise up to the surface. "I can't be open to life. That sounds like I will be doing nothing. Besides, I will just be a doormat! Either bad things will happen or nothing will happen." Now, however, Rose can feel how these thoughts tighten her rather than opening her, and she easily sees that they are not true. She recognizes that they come from fear, and she reminds herself that being open to life doesn't mean letting life run her over. In fact it is the opposite. Being open is about being actively engaged with life, responding to it rather than reacting, and allowing her responses to come from the empowered wisdom within her.

A wonderful realization comes to her and fills her with joy. She is not responsible *for* her life. That was just a game of the mind that kept her caught in struggle. As long as she was trying to create a particular kind of life, she was *missing* life. Her new task is to be responsible *to* her life by showing up for the life she has been given with passionate curiosity, rather than always struggling to make it be a particular way.

She then has the thought, "*Responsibility* doesn't mean I have to do 'it' and do 'it' right (or thus I am doing it wrong). It simply means being 'able to respond.' With a grounded awareness she sees that her task is to be responsible to what is right now. It becomes clear to her that this is the opposite of how she had lived while caught in her mind. She was lost in its core game, the game of wanting what is not here and not wanting what is.

As she looks across the field toward the village, the words *don't know* come to her as a healing balm. When she was caught in the village of Mind, those words created fear and frustration, but now they come from her wisdom self. "I truly don't know what will happen in my life, and I don't need to know. My life will unfold the way it needs to. Having to know kept me caught in my head. Not needing to know keeps me open to the great mystery of life."

She knows as she enters the village again she

will meet different challenges, each one bringing a gift. She feels a fierce commitment to giving her attention to everything inside her that still reacts so that she can see through the game of struggle and show up for life. Then she will be able to use the resources of her mind in a way that is truly healing for everyone, including herself.

As Rose turns back to bow in gratitude to the forest and her friends, she notices one of the trees that captured her attention when she was sitting on the bench, a tree that taught her about the circle of giving and receiving at the heart of life. After this sacred time in the forest, she now understands the fullness of this circle. And she sees that in opening to life, she is more interested in giving than in getting. This is so different from how she used to live in the village of Mind. When she was lost in her mind, her main desire was to get more of whatever she longed for—more treats from the bakery, more experiences, more money, more wisdom, more sex, more, more, more, and that this never brought her the deep satisfaction she longed for.

Now she knows a way of being that sees giving and receiving as two sides of the same coin. She sees that the greatest gift she has to give is her undivided attention to whatever is happening right now and in return she receives the joy of being fully awake to life. Rather than using her mind to create a particular reality, she can use it to show up for reality—to show up for the grand adventure of her life, allowing it step-by-step to bring her home.

Whenever the old reactive walls of Mind start to rebuild themselves and she begins to lose sight of all the wisdom she has received from the Magical Forest, Rose can stop for a moment, take a breath, and connect with the wisdom that is now within her. She can remember that her life is *for* her; that it is safe to experience whatever she is experiencing; that she can give her challenges the light of her attention rather than falling into them or running away; that everything is okay as it is, and that it will be okay, no matter what is happening. Most important, she now knows that she can ask for clarity and that life will live the answer through her. So she then asks life, "As I return to the village of Mind, show me what to say, do, or be in any situation that will be for the highest good." With deep certainty she knows that life will show her the way.

Now that she is fully willing to show up for her

life with curiosity and compassion, Rose knows it is time to bring her awakened heart into the village of Mind. She stands up and bows to the lion, tiger, and bear. Then with a lilt in her step, a lightness in her being, and the phrase "Right now, this is life, and it's okay!" firmly planted in her heart, she walks across the field and into the village of Mind, bringing all the gifts of the Magical Forest of Aliveness with her.

The End

About the Author

Mary O'Malley is a counselor, group facilitator and public speaker living and working in Kirkland, Washington.

Mary has more than twenty-five years' experience in the field of awakening, based on a lifetime pursuit of discovering how to be a truly awake and alive human being. Having walked the path she offers to others, she carries a passionate commitment to inviting people into the joy and the creativity of being fully awake to life.

Many people she has counseled and taught asked her to write down what she was sharing, and in the mid 1990's her first book, *Belonging to Life: The Journey of Awakening,* began to take shape. She grew immensely from this process, and her ability to speak the truth of present-moment awareness became clearer and simpler.

As Mary invited others into being present for life, it became clear to her that people need to become familiar with the stories in their heads that keep them disconnected from life. She realized that one of the best places to see and then to transform this tendency to disconnect was around compulsions, and she began to develop a ground-breaking approach for working with compulsions that not only heals the need to be compulsive in the first place, but also uncovers the wellspring of deep wisdom underlying all compulsions that can guide us into joy, peace, and freedom. Since then she has refined these ideas in groups, individual counseling sessions, and retreats, and from this her second book, *The Gift of Our Compulsions: A Revolutionary Approach to Self-Acceptance and Healing,* was born in 2004.

Mary continues to lead weekly groups both in person and on the phone. She also holds retreats both in the Northwest and in exotic places such as Hawaii and Bali. She is available for individual counseling in person and on the phone.

Information about Mary's books, CDs, groups, and retreats can be found on her website at www.maryomalley.com.

Endorsements

Be careful! After reading this little story you may be out of your mind. In fact, with any luck you will be. Here is a wonderful piece of wisdom, sent, it would seem, from life itself TO life itself, and meant for every child and adult who picks up this book. A marvelous tale about the "stuff no one ever told us," but that would have changed our lives if they had, this small volume is bound to be among the treasured literature of every household into which it is introduced --- which I hope will be many.

—**Neale Donald Walsch**, author of *Conversations with God*

Mary O'Malley is a leading light and brilliant teacher in the field of inner healing and transformation. Her powerful insights into our relationship with compulsions have served many people in a beautiful and profound way.

You'll be delighted by her wonderful new book, The Magical Forest of Aliveness. It's a sweet, simple, and wise poetic journey into human awakening that calms the mind, warms the heart, and speaks directly to the soul. Mary offers us words that nourish to the core...

—**Marc David** – Founder & Director of The Institute for the Psychology of Eating, and author of *Nourishing Wisdom and The Slow Down Diet*

Life is calling us to awaken. After reading books of greater volume and complexity, you may be deceived by the size of this little fable. Don't be. It packs a punch and provides a powerful metaphor to illuminate the steps on your journey of awakening. The Magical Forest of Aliveness is an important story for adults as it equips your inner child with metaphors to lead the way in your own awakening – and to stay awake. For those of you who are parents, it provides metaphor and wisdom to assist you in raising conscious children. Conscious adults and conscious children in an awakening world – how good can it get? Mary has penned another masterpiece.

—**Rev. Deborah Olive**, Unity Minister, co-chair of the Spiritual Social Action Ministry Team for the Association of Unity Churches International and co-host of "A World That Works" on Unity FM.

Mary O'Malley's allegory of Awakening breathes the magic of life back into our consciousness even within the first few paragraphs of this sweet and intriguing and life-affirming fairy tale. Suddenly everything around us is vibrating with light; with love; with the conspicuous benevolence of which Life has always hoped we'd take notice.

In my view, this is one of the clearest, most easily understood stories to be found on the topic of Awakening. It can be shared with children and adults alike, and I believe that it should be -- and that it should be read often.

—**Em Claire**, American-born poet and author of the poetic compendium *Silent Sacred Holy Deepening Heart*"